Introduction

The purpose of a box of crayons is to bring color and life into lifeless images. An object appears colored because of the way it interacts with light. The color itself comes from the light. The blue crayon is only blue because of the amount of light that is present, absorbed, and reflected off the crayon. Without light, there is no color.

One of the first things the Bible tells us is God made light.

> And God said, "Let there be light," and there was light.
> - Genesis 1:3 (NIV)

Prior to God speaking light into existence, He had created the Earth, but it was empty. It was missing something.

> In the beginning, God created the heavens and the earth. 2
> Now the earth was formless and empty, darkness was over the
> surface of the deep, and the Spirit of God was hovering over
> the waters. - Genesis 1:1-2 (NIV)

That is when God created color. He sent light to fill up the Earth and started coloring the rest of the Earth in. He added details of land, plants, fruit, stars, and zebras. Yet God still did not feel His picture was complete.

> Then God said, "Let us make mankind in our image, in our
> likeness, so that they may rule over the fish in the sea and the
> birds in the sky, over the livestock and all the wild animals, and
> over all the creatures that move along the ground."
> - Genesis 1:26 (NIV)

God created His greatest masterpiece, us. Later in the Bible, Jesus further defined our role on this Earth.

> 14-16 "Here's another way to put it: You're here to be light,
> bringing out the God-colors in the world. God is not a secret to
> be kept. We're going public with this, as public as a city on a hill.
> If I make you light-bearers, you don't think I'm going to hide
> you under a bucket, do you? I'm putting you on a light stand.
> Now that I've put you there on a hilltop, on a light stand—shine!
> - Matthew 5:14-15 (Message)

We are God's crayons! He wants us to color this world by shining light on every part.

> And the Good News about the Kingdom will be preached
> throughout the whole world, so that all nations will hear it; and
> then the end will come. - Matthew 24:14 (NLT)

Our mission is to color the entire world. I am excited to color this world with you because God is light, He is color, God is Like a Box of Crayons.

God is Like a Box of Crayons

God is Like a Box of Crayons

Explainer

Before we jump into the rest of the book I want to make sure you understand my heart behind comparing the God of a universe to an inanimate crayon.

God is so much more than any physical object can describe, but by looking at different things and looking for how they reflect God's design and heart we become better at seeing God in everything around us.

> For ever since the creation of the world His invisible attributes,
> His eternal power and divine nature, have been clearly seen,
> being understood through His workmanship [all His creation,
> the wonderful things that He has made], so that they [who fail
> to believe and trust in Him] are without excuse and without
> defense. - Romans 1:20 (Amp)

I believe that looking to things outside of ourselves and asking what they can teach us about God will help us understand Him more.

> However, call on the animals to teach you; the birds that sail
> through the air are not afraid to tell you the truth. 8 Engage
> the earth in conversation; it's happy to share what it knows.
> Even the fish of the sea are wise enough to explain it to you. 9
> In fact, which part of creation isn't aware, which doesn't
> know the Eternal's hand has done this?
> - Job 12:7-10 (Voice)

Lastly, I also want to use things that you will encounter in your life to trigger a thought about God. We are surrounded by negative stories, disasters, sadness, and hopelessness and I want to remind you of the good things as you walk through life.

> Finally, brothers and sisters, fill your minds with beauty and
> truth. Meditate on whatever is honorable, whatever is right,
> whatever is pure, whatever is lovely, whatever is good,
> whatever is virtuous and praiseworthy. - Philippians 4:8 (Voice)

I encourage you to look for God all around you, because the more you do, the more you flex your God sight muscles, the easier it becomes to see God.

I hope this book and all the books in the God is Like Devotional series will help you see God in everything around you. Because devotions should never be boring.

God is Like a Box of Crayons

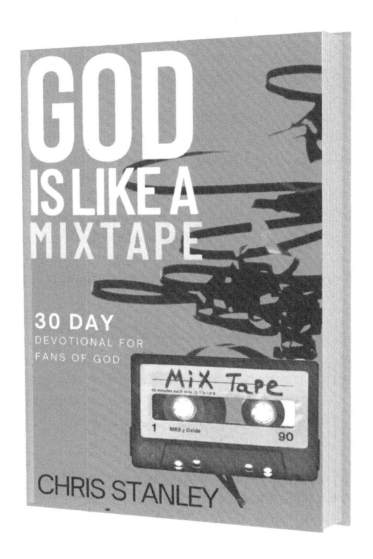

Get a Free Devotional by Heading to

GodisLikea.com/free/

Get our God Is Like a Mixtape devotional book for free when you join the "God is Like" email list.

Bluetiful

Throughout history, blue pigments are notoriously unstable and subject to fading. The YInMn blue pigment that inspired this crayon is safer, lasts longer, and is a near-perfect blue color when compared with other blue pigments. Professor Mas Subramanian and one of his students, Andrew E. Smith, discovered how to create it at Oregon State University on accident in 2009.

Prior to the creation of this new pigment, the last blue pigment to be discovered was cobalt blue in 1802. The issue with the cobalt blue pigment, as well as suffering from the same fading issues we know blue pigments for, it's also poisonous. This new blue, Bluetiful, is a blue that promises it will stand the test of time.

One way or another we know this blue will not last, though. Like everything else on this planet and in our lives, one day it will fade. It will go away. It will be destroyed. This is something we get used to. Things break, they don't maintain their shine.
Our world is broken. We are all fading towards death, slowly dying, but God promises us something that will never fade.

> Praise be to the God and Father of our Lord Jesus Christ! In his great mercy he has given us new birth into a living hope through the resurrection of Jesus Christ from the dead, 4 and into an inheritance that can never perish, spoil or fade. This inheritance is kept in heaven for you,
> - 1 Peter 1:3-4 (NIV)

Although our lives will fade away, we have an eternal destiny with God. He loves us enough to reserve a place for us, to call us His kids, and let us inherit everything that He has.

> Eternal One: Now look here! I am creating new heavens and a new earth. The weary and painful past will be as if it never happened. No one will talk or even think about it anymore.
>
> 18 So take joy and celebrate with unending gladness on account of what I am creating. Look carefully! I am making this place I've chosen, this Jerusalem, a city of joy. I'm making her citizens, My people, a people of gladness.
>
> 19 This Jerusalem, My pride and joy, and her people will be a delight to Me. Though you listen at every corner, You will never hear crying, never hear despair or grief.
> - Isaiah 65:17-19 (The Voice)

Just like the Bluetiful color represents a promise of an enduring blue, so too does God give us a promise of something that will never fade, a future home that will be perfect. It will be Bluetiful.

God is Like a Box of Crayons

God is Like a Box of Crayons

Yellow

There is something about the color yellow that just screams "Hey look over here, smile!"
The color yellow is used to color the sun, smiling faces, bananas, baby chicks, lemonade, stars, and, of course, duckies.

We know yellow as the color of optimism. It represents happiness and joy. Who can color a rubber duckie yellow without smiling, not me. They've proven it boosts curiosity and brings fun and joy to the world.

Interestingly enough, it is so good at getting people's attention. We also use it as a color of warning. Our world is a dark place. Sad things happen, people treat each other badly, and often we need a bright spot to bring some optimism into our lives.
Jesus called us to be that hope, to bring that optimism, to be yellow in a dark world. Jesus called us to be a bright spot in a dark place.

> "You are the light of the world. A town built on a hill cannot be hidden. Neither do people light a lamp and put it under a bowl. Instead, they put it on its stand and it gives light to everyone in the house. In the same way let your light shine before others that they may be see your good deeds and glorify your father in heaven." - Matthew 5:14-16

Jesus called us to be yellow on this Earth, provide light, do good deeds, directing people back to Him for hope, a promise, a God who loves them.

For some, this will evoke feelings of anxiety. If there is a God, He will hold us all accountable. We are a reminder that judgment is coming, a reminder to repent, a reminder that there is more than what's on the surface. We are a warning sign.

Just like yellow is used to bring optimism, fun, and joy to a coloring page, or a warning, so too does God use us to be a bright spot that lifts the spirits of others and warns them of things to come.

God is Like a Box of Crayons

Green

Green, the color of life, health, plants and trees. Many eating lifestyles have presented themselves over the years, but getting back to eating more greens and no meat has become increasingly popular.

We associate vegetarian and vegan lifestyles with a lower risk of many chronic illnesses. Things like heart disease, high blood pressure, cancer, and obesity all are less likely for vegetarian eaters. Eating leafy greens also helps the body restore the immune system and repair body tissue.

A foodie and hard-core carnivore, like myself, chuckles at such a notion. Give up meat? God loved meat! He had us do all those sacrifices in the Bible and it said He loved meat.

> Then Noah built an altar to the Lord and took some of every clean animal and some of every clean bird and offered burnt offerings on the altar. 21 And when the Lord smelled the pleasing aroma...
> - Genesis 8:20-21 (ESV)

Exactly, a pleasing aroma, one that I will enjoy and put onto my plate for dinner because God said I could, so it is healthy, right?

Back in the beginning, God had designed a perfect world. A world where we lived in harmony with the animals of the wild, even with the lions and snakes. This design didn't include us eating a cow, but harvesting green plants from the plentiful Garden.

> And God said, "Behold, I have given you every plant yielding seed that is on the face of all the earth, and every tree with seed in its fruit. You shall have them for food. And to every beast of the earth and to every bird of the heavens and to everything that creeps on the earth, everything that has the breath of life, I have given every green plant for food.
> - Genesis 1:29-30 (ESV)

I will still eat a juicy burger stacked with some wonderful plants from the garden, but the color green makes me wonder if as we pursue perfection through Jesus in our souls, perhaps our bodies are longing for perfection in a change of diet.

Just like green food is the key to a healthy body, so too is God the key to a healthy soul.

> The Lord is my shepherd; I shall not want.2 He makes me lie down in green pastures. He leads me beside still waters.3 He restores my soul... - Psalm 23:1-3 (ESV)

God is Like a Box of Crayons

God is Like a Box of Crayons

Black

The darkest of colors, the true anti-color, is black. Something is colored black because it absorbs all light and does not reflect any light back. Black is the absence of light.

Most of us are apprehensive to be out, wandering in the dark of night. We feel uncomfortable and find ourselves looking behind us and wondering what is beyond our sight and hoping we can find our way back.

Our world and our hearts are dark, full of sin. We fear becoming lost in our past mistakes. The darkness in the world presses in and sometimes it feels like darkness has won.

> But if your eye is clouded or evil, then your body will be filled with evil and dark clouds. And the darkness that takes over the body of a child of God who has gone astray—that is the deepest, darkest darkness there is. - Matthew 6:23

But darkness hasn't won!

> In the beginning, was the Word, and the Word was with God, and the Word was God. 2 He was in the beginning with God.
>
> 3 All things were made through him, and without him was not any thing made that was made. 4 In him was life, and the life was the light of men. 5 The light shines in the darkness, and the darkness has not overcome it.- John 1:1-5 (ESV)

God is light, and He penetrates everything. No matter how far you feel you've gone from God, how dark your situation may feel, God is there, radiating, waiting for you to allow His light to shine on you.

> This is the message we have heard from him and declare to you: God is light; in him there is no darkness at all...If we confess our sins, he is faithful and just and will forgive us our sins and purify us from all unrighteousness.- 1 John 1:5-9

When you feel the darkness closing in on your heart, confess your sins, run to the light! He has never left you and will shine His light of grace into even the darkest of sins.

Just like the color black is the lack of light, so too is our sin a lack of God's presence in our actions but He is ready to illuminate our deeds so they can shine pure, reflecting His righteousness into the world.

God is Like a Box of Crayons

God is Like a Box of Crayons

White

White, the color of purity, the perfect unblemished color.

To recreate the color white on a screen, the combination of all colors is used to create the perception of white. White, though, is technically not even a color.

Pure white is not common in our world. Sheep's wool, a dove, a blanket of snow, seashells, the clouds in the sky, are riddled with imperfections. The purer the white, the more inspiring of a sight it is.

White is the opposite of the color black. White reflects the light that shines on it, while black absorbs it.

When God says,

> Though your sins are like scarlet, They shall be as white as
> snow; Though they are red like crimson, They shall be as wool.
> - Isaiah 1:18 (NKJV)

He is saying that He will make you a great reflection of Him! He will shine His light on you and you will reflect Him to the world. God is a perfect balance of all the colors, traits, and personalities. When you reflect these, you shine white. You will be a sight as inspiring as a perfect snowscape that will remind people of their creator.

God is preparing us, refining us, and cleansing us of all our wrongdoing, so we will be ready when He sends His son to bring us into our forever home.

Just like white is light-reflecting, so too is God making us pure and white as snow to reflect Him into the world.

God is Like a Box of Crayons

Red

Red jumps out at us. It is the first color, other than black and white that babies can see. Inside the womb, babies can detect light and shadows, and when they are born, they can make out shapes where the light and dark meet.

A few weeks into their life, suddenly out of the light and dark, the vibrant red color emerges. This happens with our spiritual eyesight as well. Inevitably in our lives, we are walking through life oblivious to an all-powerful, almighty God who sits on a throne of judgment.

We are unaware that he is aware of everything that we do. We know that there are morals. We know we shouldn't kill someone. We believe that stealing is not a good idea, but it's just shadows. We don't really have a clear picture of sin. It is why God created the law, to make it clear what was right and what was wrong, white from black.

> Therefore no one will be declared righteous in God's sight by
> the works of the law; rather, through the law we become
> conscious of our sin. - Romans 3:20 (NIV)

Once we are birthed into a new life with Christ when we become aware and can see clearly black and white, sin and God. Black and white are the first colors we see. We realize our filth. We realize how messy we are and how perfect God is. We realize we need forgiveness for our sins.

Hebrews 9 states,

> "Under the law, it's almost the case that everything is purifed in
> connection with blood; without the shedding of blood, sin
> cannot be forgiven." - Hebrews 9:22 (Voice)

This is when the third color emerges, red. We now realize someone has to pay for our wrongs. But who? How? How can we make things right?

> "then how much more powerful is the blood of the Anointed
> One, who through the eternal spirit offered Himself as a
> spotless sacrifice to God, purifying your conscience from the
> dead things of the world to the service of the living God?"
> - Hebrews 9:14 (VOICE)

That's when our true conversion happens. It's when we realize we've failed and we can't fix it. It's when we realize that only one person can, Jesus.

Just like a baby first can see light and dark before seeing red, so too do we, as humans, have to see God's light and realize our darkness so we can then see Jesus's red blood and why it matters.

God is Like a Box of Crayons

God is Like a Box of Crayons

Orange

This bright color was named after the orange fruit, a source of vitamin C. We are told we need this invisible nutrient, but why? What does Vitamin C do for us?

During the age of discovery, from the 15th to the 18th century, 2 million people died from vitamin C deficiency. As explorers crossed vast oceans and looked to the great beyond they didn't know why they kept getting sick. It turns out it was from a lack of vitamin C. They called the disease scurvy.

When you are in short supply of vitamin C, your body falls apart. Without vitamin C, you can no longer produce collagen, the glue that keeps your body's cells together. Old wounds reappear, previously broken bones are once again broken. Parts of your body, like your gums, putrefy and turn black, all because you are lacking in Vitamin C. The glue that held you together is gone.

When we look at our world, we see it falling apart. Old wounds of hate, racism, division, and despair are reappearing. We don't see orange when we look out into the world. We see things turning black. Maybe it's time to look to something brighter, something orange that contains the nutrients for healing.

> "He is the exact image of the invisible God, the firstborn of creation, the eternal. It was by Him that everything was created: the heavens, the earth, all the things within and upon them, all things seen and unseen, thrones and dominions, spiritual powers and authorites. Every detail was crafted through His design, by His own hands and for his purposes. He has always been! It is His hands that holds everything together." - Colossians 1:15-17

The glue that is missing from our world is missing because we are missing the key ingredient. Jesus, the king of the universe.

Paul reminds us again in Hebrews,

> "The Son perfectly mirrors God and is stamped with God's nature. He holds everything together by what he says-powerful words." - Hebrews 1:2-3 (Message)

We need more of Jesus, more of His words in our lives and in our world. Because just like an orange holds the secret ingredient to our body holding itself together, so too is God the ingredient that keeps our world from falling apart.

God is Like a Box of Crayons

Purple

In the past, kings and queens have outlawed the wearing purple by peasants and at other times could not afford it themselves.

The dye to make purple was once so expensive a purple scarf literally cost its weight in gold. Unfortunately, the Roman Emperor Aurelian will go down in history as the man who had to tell his wife "no" to that scarf. The third century was apparently brutal for window shopping.

The Bible paints a picture of Jesus being anointed as King of the Jews.

> Then Pilate took Jesus and had him flogged. The soldiers twisted together a crown of thorns and put it on his head. They clothed him in a purple robe...
>
> When Jesus came out wearing the crown of thorns and the purple robe. Pilate said... "Shall I crucify your king?" "We have no king but Caesar," the chief priests answered.- John 19:1-16 (NIV)

Those very people God sent His son to save, rejected Jesus, the humble king of mankind, King of the Jews, dripping blood, adorned in a kingly purple robe. While the Jews may have denied Jesus His place as their king, He is coming back with another robe to claim His throne.

> "I saw heaven standing open and there before me was a white horse, whose rider is called Faithful and True. With justice he judges and wages war. His eyes are like a blazing fire and on his head are many crowns... He is dressed in a robe dipped in blood, and his name is the Word of God." - Revelation 19:11-13

They forced Jesus to wear a bloody robe the first time, but He embraced that look and when he comes back, he'll be wearing a robe covered in blood to get His people.

Just like purple is the color that signifies royalty and kings, so too a purple robe signifies Jesus is our king of kings and Lord of Lords.

God is Like a Box of Crayons

Brown

When I see brown, I instantly think of dirt and soil. I smell the freshly turned earth of a garden. I think of my own children playing in the dirt. Digging holes, building castles, creating. We, as modern adults, interact less with dirt as time goes on. We wonder at the free spirit of a child who can take dirt and throw it on their head, rub it in their face, and give a smile that warms your heart.

My oldest loved to eat dirt, shoved it by the fistful into his mouth. People would look over at us, concerned as if with a silent question.

"Are you going to stop him?"

If we answered the quiet question we'd said, "God made dirt and dirt don't hurt."

Recently we visited a beach and my wife formed the shape of a turtle with her hands. She molded the sand into a beautiful sand sculpture. She carefully added a texture to the turtle's shell until she was happy with her creation.

In Genesis, we see God, the maker of the universe, kneeling down and playing with dirt to create His greatest creation.

> "One day the Eternal God scooped dirt out of the ground,
> sculpted it into the shape we call human, breathed the breath
> that gives life into the nostrils of the human, and the human
> became a living soul." - Genesis 2:7 (Voice)

God not only made dirt, but he made us out of the dirt. He got His hands dirty. He embraced the mess and molded us with infinite care into something He loved.

But He didn't stop there. He bent down and put His mouth to the dirt. His perfect lips that spoke our universe into existence touched dirt, touched us, so we could have life and live with Him.

We often picture God as something that is far away, sitting on a huge throne, far away from us. We imagine He rules with an iron fist, throwing lightning bolts from His fingers. We envision Him as above it all and not in the muck and mire of life. Maybe we should have a different perspective. Maybe we should envision Him bent over in the dirt, bent over in the muck of life, carving out our existence.

Just like we make sand sculptures and sometimes end up with brown dirt in our mouth, so too did God sculpt us out of the dirt and put his mouth to dirt to give us life.

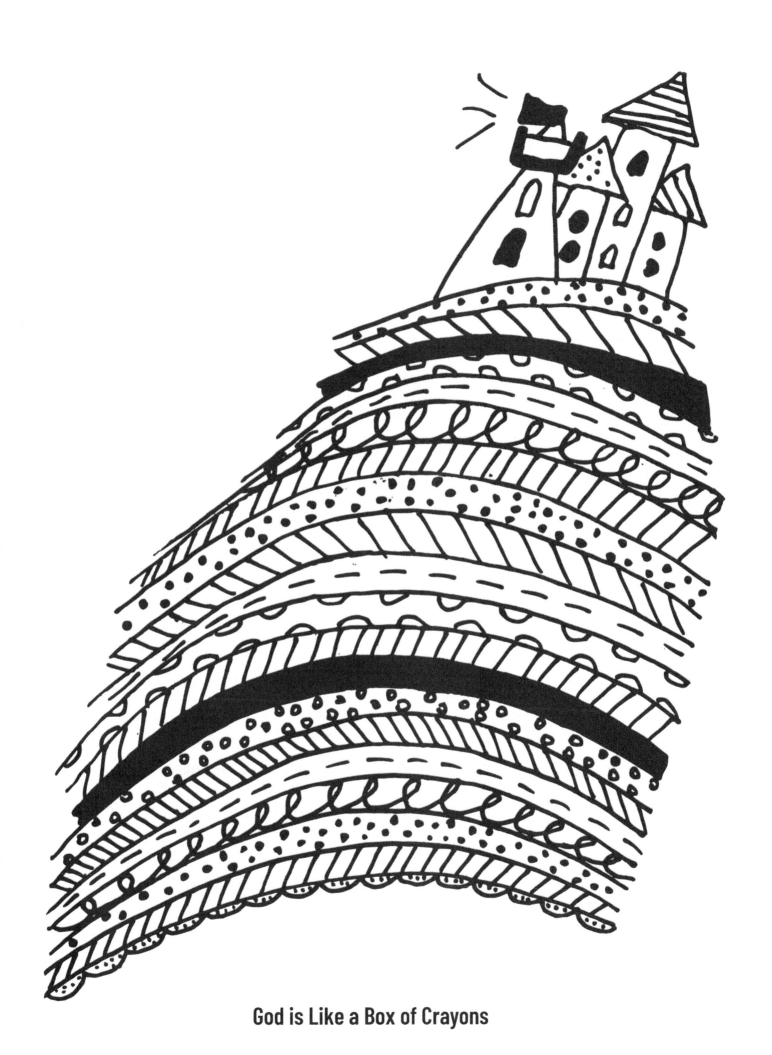

God is Like a Box of Crayons

Tumbleweed

They named the color tumbleweed after the dried and uprooted plant that is tossed across desert plains. Although tumbleweeds aren't native to the United States, most of us think of wild west movies when we hear the word tumbleweed. You might have heard western music in your head the moment you read the title of this devotional.

The tumbleweed that we are thinking about originated in Russia. Russian thistle seeds contaminated a bag of flaxseed that arrived in South Dakota in 1873, and the plant has spread across the United States ever since.

While tumbleweeds are not native to America, they are native to the Judean Desert. These tumbleweeds are the Desert Rose plant. This desert has special significance because Jesus and Satan had their own wild west showdown there.

> Next Jesus was taken into the wild by the Spirit for the Test. The Devil was ready to give it. Jesus prepared for the Test by fasting forty days and forty nights. That left him, of course, in a state of extreme hunger, which the Devil took advantage of in the first test: "Since you are God's Son, speak the word that will turn these stones into loaves of bread." 4 Jesus answered by quoting Deuteronomy: "It takes more than bread to stay alive. It takes a steady stream of words from God's mouth." - Matthew 4:1-3 (Message)

First shots fired, but Satan didn't stop. He loaded another round.

> For the second test, the Devil took him to the Holy City. He sat him on top of the Temple and said, "Since you are God's Son, jump." The Devil goaded him by quoting Psalm 91: "He has placed you in the care of angels. They will catch you so that you won't so much as stub your toe on a stone." 7 Jesus countered with another citation from Deuteronomy: "Don't you dare test the Lord your God."
> - Matthew 4:5-7 (Message)

One round left in the chamber for this wild west shootout. Satan attempts to bribe Jesus.

> For the third test, the Devil took him to the peak of a huge mountain. He gestured expansively, pointing out all the earth's kingdoms, how glorious they all were. Then he said, "They're yours—lock, stock, and barrel. Just go down on your knees and worship me, and they're yours." - Matthew 4:8-9 (Message)

I imagine Jesus took a deep breath, and His life flashed before His eyes. He probably pictured what His ministry would look like, His future disciples, and all the pain He would go through on the cross. He probably pictured you. If He owned the world, He wouldn't have to go through the pain of the cross, but only He would be saved. You wouldn't be.
Jesus grits His teeth and His eyes flash open.

> Jesus' refusal was curt: "Beat it, Satan!" He backed his rebuke with a third quotation from Deuteronomy: "Worship the Lord your God, and only him. Serve him with absolute single-heartedness." 11 The Test was over. The Devil left. And in his place, angels! Angels came and took care of Jesus' needs.- Matthew 4:10-11 (Message)

Just like the color tumbleweed makes us think of wild west showdowns, so too should they remind us of the ultimate desert showdown that Jesus had against Satan.

God is Like a Box of Crayons

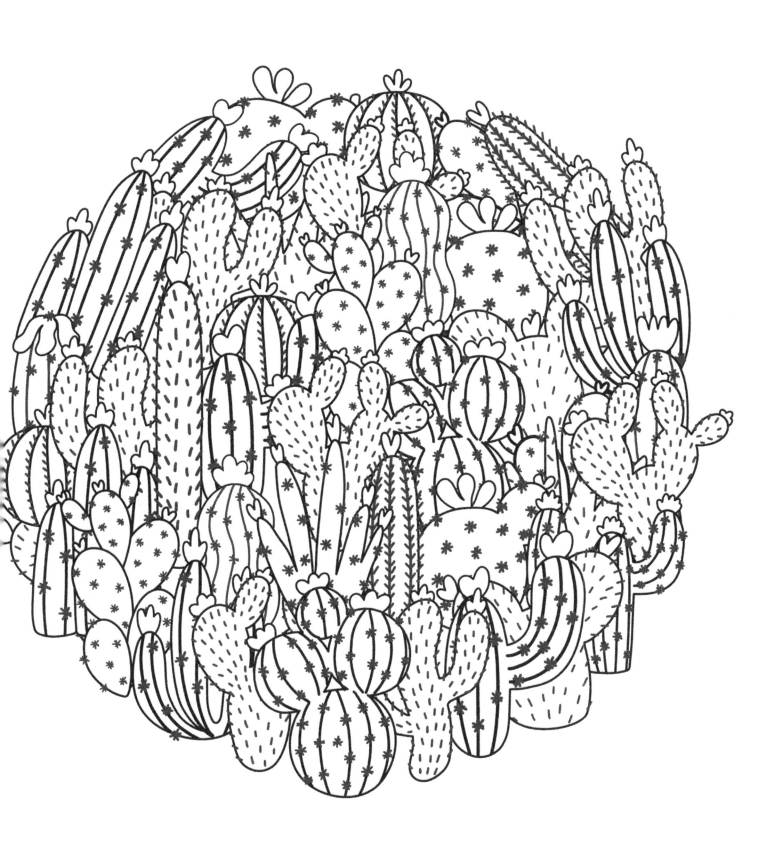

God is Like a Box of Crayons

Periwinkle

This color is named after the periwinkle flower. A viny plant that is evergreen and blossoms lovely flowers in the spring.

We have used this evergreen plant throughout history as adornment on special occasions. One claim to periwinkle fame comes from a famous wedding poem.

"Something new, Something borrowed, Something blue..."

They believe the blue in the poem to be periwinkle. Women have used the blue flower as a garter, hoping to have a fertile marriage.

In medieval times, they also used periwinkle as a symbol of Jesus and a reminder of heaven. God is preparing us for our wedding day with His son Jesus by giving us something new, something borrowed, and something blue.

First He is giving us a new heart that is full of love for His son.

And I will give you a new heart, and I will put a new spirit in you. I will take out your stony, stubborn heart and give you a tender, responsive heart.
- Ezekiel 36:26 (NLT)

God has allowed us to borrow His precious words and the faith that comes from believing. He allows us to see the truth of who Jesus is and entrusts us to hold onto that until Christ returns.

Remember the words that you heard from me. Retain them as the model for healthy and sound teaching in the faith and love that are available in Jesus the Anointed. 14 As for the precious thing entrusted to you, protect it with the help of the Holy Spirit who dwells within us. - 2 Timothy 1:13-14 (Voice)

Lastly, what has God given us that is blue? According to scholars, blue represents the Holy Spirit. God not only changed our hearts, but He also gave us a special present. His helper, the Holy Spirit living inside of us. God gave us something blue.

The Father is sending a great Helper, the Holy Spirit, in My name to teach you everything and to remind you of all I have said to you.- John 14:26 (Voice)

When life feels dark, pointless, and destroyed, we need to be reminded that this isn't all there is. We have a marriage date set with Jesus. With this knowledge, we can walk through our days with a periwinkle and the gifts that God has given us.

Just like periwinkle is an answer for a bride to have something new, something borrowed, and something blue, God is the answer we need to be ready for our marriage day.

God is Like a Box of Crayons

God is Like a Box of Crayons

Goldenrod

The color goldenrod is a vivid yellow and orange. They named it after a flower. There are other bright yellow flowers that pop up throughout the year, but this flower is especially important.

For the Southern part of the United States, the goldenrod flower is the last true nectar and pollen source of the year for honeybees. This last big batch of sustenance allows the honeybees to stock up for winter just before the weather turns cold. The extra supplies prompt the queen to produce more brood, or baby bees, that will help the hive stay warm. Bees can't leave their hive, they are prisoners inside during the cold season. It is dark, frigid, and the bees are working hard to survive. The extra honey helps ensure they'll have the energy to push through.

The surplus nectar also allows the bees to cap their honeycomb. This is like putting a lid on a jar. It keeps the comb from drying up, molding, or spoiling. This fresh supply of food keeps the hive healthy throughout the winter, all thanks to the goldenrod flower.

The apostle Paul tells us that God is the same way.

> You can be sure that God will take care of everything you need,
> his generosity exceeding even yours in the glory that pours
> from Jesus.- Philippians 4:19 (Message)

Yes, we know that God can take care of us, but we still worry about how we'll feed the family, pay the heating bill, or push through a difficult season of work.

> "If God gives such attention to the appearance of wildflowers—most of which are never even seen—don't you think he'll attend to you, take pride in you, do his best for you?
>
> What I'm trying to do here is to get you to relax, to not be so preoccupied with getting, so you can respond to God's giving. People who don't know God and the way he works fuss over these things, but you know both God and how he works. Steep your life in God-reality, God-initiative, God-provisions.
>
> Don't worry about missing out. You'll find all your everyday human concerns will be met. "Give your entire attention to what God is doing right now, and don't get worked up about what may or may not happen tomorrow. God will help you deal with whatever hard things come up when the time comes.
> - Matthew 6:30-34 (Message)

Just like the goldenrod supplies the food for the honeybees searching out the season's last flowers, so too does God promise to fortify us against the cold if we seek Him out.

God is Like a Box of Crayons

God is Like a Box of Crayons

Olive Green

When most people think of olives and the Bible, the image of an olive branch comes to mind. Noah floating on the waters and a dove bringing Him a branch. We think of Jesus providing us peace, but olives are much more than just their branches. The olive tree is more than just peace.

The food that the olive branch holds is a life and death matter. Commonly thought to be a vegetable, olives are actually fruits. This fruit is considered a staple food. The world uses the oil extracted from the olive fruit in significant amounts, consuming 2.25 million liters of olive oil each year. Without the calories from staple foods, billions would starve.

When someone is starving they need food. Peace sounds nice, but give me some food. Our souls are spiritually starving. We are hungry for something and searching for it.

> He humbled you and allowed you to be hungry and fed you with manna, [a substance] which you did not know, nor did your fathers know, so that He might make you understand [by personal experience] that man does not live by bread alone, but man lives by every word that proceeds out of the mouth of the Lord. - Deuteronomy 8:3 (Amp)

The words of God give us life, but where do we get these words? Where can we find the food?

> In the beginning [before all time] was the Word (Christ), and the Word was with God, and the Word was God Himself. 2 He was [continually existing] in the beginning [co-eternally] with God. - John 1:1-2 (Amp)

Jesus has the food because He is the living word of God. If we follow Jesus we'll never be spiritually hungry again.

> I am the bread that gives life. If you come to My table and eat, you will never go hungry. Believe in Me, and you will never go thirsty.- John 6:35 (Voice)

Just like olives feed the world as a staple food, so too does God feed our souls with the word of God, Jesus Christ.

God is Like a Box of Crayons

Bittersweet

Why would anyone make something bittersweet? Can I order the bittersweet, but hold the bitter and add extra sweet, please?

The reality is we love bittersweet things. Lemonade on a summer day, dark chocolate during movie night, or cranberries at Thanksgiving. Need I go on?

What makes all of these delightful tastes work is the contrast. The tart and bitter lemon contrasts the smooth sweetness of sugar. in lemonade. We could just drink sugar water, but the contrast brings out the sweetness and makes us enjoy the drink. No one wants to drink sugar water, but when you add lemons it makes us enjoy the sweetness.

Life is also bittersweet. We have death, pain, and sickness around us each and every day. We have joys of marriage, first steps, puppy dogs, and salvation that lift our spirits.

Without the bitter in life, we couldn't fully appreciate the sweet things that God has given us. If we didn't know we needed grace or mercy, we wouldn't value them when Jesus gave them to us.
If God wasn't going to judge the entire planet for our sins, we wouldn't experience the sweetness of forgiveness. John, the author of Revelation experiences that bittersweet revelation of God's impending judgment.

The words of God give us life, but where do we get these words? Where can we find the food?

> So I went to the angel and asked him to give me the little scroll. He said to me, "Take it and eat it. It will turn your stomach sour, but 'in your mouth it will be as sweet as honey. - Revelation 10:9-10 (NIV)

The bitterness of our sins and failures is what makes God's forgiveness so sweet.

> Blessed is the one whose transgressions are forgiven,   whose sins are covered.
> - Psalm 32:1 (NIV)

> She was forgiven many, many sins, and so she is very, very grateful. If the forgiveness is minimal, the gratitude is minimal.- Luke 4:47(MSG)

Just like bitter reveals the sweet in food, so too does the reality of God's judgment reveal to us the sweet relief for His forgiveness of our sins.

God is Like a Box of Crayons

God is Like a Box of Crayons

Mahogany

The sun beats down on you; you feel your skin burning. You've drunk your last bit of water and you've got more miles more to go. You see a spot off the path, with the most glorious sight you can imagine... shade.

One of the best trees for shade in South Florida or the Caribbean is mahogany.

We often overlook shade when it is readily available and long for it earnestly when it is lacking.
In our own lives, we feel over-exposed to the heat of life. We feel like we can't take another moment of the intensity. It is in these moments that we need and find relief.

"Have mercy on me O God, have mercy on me for the hope of my soul is in you. I will keep myself safely under the shade of your wings till these troubles are past."
- Psalm 57:1

As you trudge through your trials and you feel unprotected and can't take the elements of life, hear the words that King David wrote,

"The Lord watches over you the Lord is your shade at your right hand, the sun will not harm you by day nor the moon by night The Lord will keep you from all harm he will watch over your life the Lord will watch over your coming and going both now and forevermore.- Psalm 121:5-8 (Voice)

Just like mahogany is the tree of choice for those enduring the heat of the day, so too is God our choice of shade in the heat of life.

God is Like a Box of Crayons

God is Like a Box of Crayons

Lavender

The lavender crayon is a soft pinkish-purple. They named it after the herb that has many uses. The name covers 47 different species of plants from the mint family.

Lavender is a very diverse plant. It has documented uses dating back 2500 years. We use it for flavoring food, healing, washing, and making things smell nice. Some say it cures headaches, relieves stress, heals insect bites, stops indigestion, sooths heartburn and sunburn.

There is a famous story of the French chemist and scholar René-Maurice Gattefossé burning his hand during an experiment and plunging in his hand into a tub of lavender oil. Not only did it help the pain, but it amazed him at how little scarring occurred.

The Romans used lavender to scent themselves, their baths, and their beds. They used lavender in a recipe to create an expensive aromatic oil known as Nard or Spikenard. Mary Magdalene used this on Jesus' feet.

> Mary therefore took a pound of expensive ointment made from pure nard, and anointed the feet of Jesus and wiped his feet with her hair. The house was filled with the fragrance of the perfume.- John 12:3 (ESV)

People who watched Mary use this costly perfume on Jesus' feet thought it was a waste of money.

> But Judas Iscariot, one of his disciples (he who was about to betray him), said, 5 "Why was this ointment not sold for three hundred denarii and given to the poor?"
> - John 12:4-5 (ESV)

Jesus defended Mary,

> Jesus said, "Leave her alone, so that she may keep it for the day of my burial. 8 For the poor you always have with you, but you do not always have me."
> - John 12:7-8 (ESV)

The symbolism is beautiful. He came to cure what ails us, to take away the pain of our world. The sin that causes the sickness of our lives. Jesus came to save us. It is fitting that lavender should adorn His body prior to Him going to the cross.

Just like lavender is used to cure ailments, so too did God send Jesus to cure our eternal ailment and to bring relief from the flames.

God is Like a Box of Crayons

God is Like a Box of Crayons

Wisteria

This purple is named after a vine and flower that belong to the legume family. Although beautiful, some gardeners hate the Chinese Wisteria plant.

It is an invasive species. Originally introduced in 1816, it has spread across America and you can find it in nineteen different states. This plant can quickly take over a yard. According to the University of Florida,

"The problem with wisteria lies in its growth habit. Wisteria is a vine that will grow virtually up anything in its path. By creating a dense canopy, it chokes out other plants. It has even been known to kill large trees. Invasive species are harmful to our natural resources because they disrupt natural communities and ecological processes."

The disruption of what is already established is where the danger of invasive species comes in. It can take what is and flip it on its head. So what qualifies as an invasive species? According to NOAA,

"An invasive species is an organism that causes ecological or economic harm in a new environment where it is not native."

By this definition, Jesus was an invasive species.

They are not of the world, just as I am not of the world.- John 17:16 (ESV)

Do you think I came to smooth things over and make everything nice? Not so. I've come to disrupt and confront!
- Luke 12:51 (Message)

11-13 A large herd of pigs was grazing and rooting on a nearby hill. The demons begged him, "Send us to the pigs so we can live in them." Jesus gave the order. But it was even worse for the pigs than for the man. Crazed, they stampeded over a cliff into the sea and drowned.14-15 Those tending the pigs, scared to death, bolted and told their story in town and country...

16-17 Those who had seen it told the others what had happened to the demon-possessed man and the pigs. At first they were in awe—and then they were upset, upset over the drowned pigs. They demanded that Jesus leave and not come back.
- Mark 5:11-17 (The Message)

Jesus came to shake up what was already established. We'd done a bang-up job, causing the world to fall into sin. Repeatedly going the wrong way and ignoring His warnings and commandments.

Think about it in your own life. If Jesus hadn't come and disrupted you and how you were living, where would you be? I shudder to think of my own path to utter destruction. Thank God for sending Jesus to disrupt my ecosystem of sin. Jesus came and created a canopy to cover up my sins and in its place put beautiful flowers of grace and mercy.

Just like the Chinese Wisteria is an invasive species that disrupts the established plants, so too did God send Jesus to disrupt everything that was established.

God is Like a Box of Crayons

God is Like a Box of Crayons

Sea Green

This color is one of my favorites. This green has a bluish tint to it and, true to its name, matches beautiful ocean conditions. It is a color that people travel the world to see.

Underneath the surface of these jewel-like waters are inspiring creatures. Animals like sea turtles, dolphins, manta rays, lobster, conch, fish and sharks make swimming an exciting experience.

Beyond these shallow waters, God filled the ocean with many more strange and wondrous creations. Vampire squids, leafy sea dragons (sea horse), Viperfish, and dumbo octopus show God has a great imagination. Science is still learning of new creatures that come up from the deep of the ocean. The ocean holds secrets to this day.

> Praise God from earth, you sea dragons, you fathomless ocean deeps;
> - Psalm 148:7 (Message)

Many believe that this reference to "sea dragons" is talking about the mighty whales in the ocean. Others believe it is referencing a more mythical sea creature, such as Leviathan. The Bible also references this creature in Job. God paints a picture of how powerful He truly is by describing a sea monster He created.

> "Can you catch Leviathan with a hook or put a noose around its jaw? Can you tie it with a rope through the nose or pierce its jaw with a spike?...7 Will its hide be hurt by spears or its head by a harpoon? 8 If you lay a hand on it, you will certainly remember the battle that follows. You won't try that again!
>
> 9 No, it is useless to capture it. The hunter who attempts it will be knocked down.10 And since no one dares to disturb it, who then can stand up to me? 11 Who has given me anything that I need to pay back? Everything under heaven is mine.
> - Job 41:1-11 (ESV)

Whether this creature is the great blue whale or another one that we've yet to discover, God is master and creator of it all.

Just like sea green inspires our imagination at what creatures the beautiful ocean holds, so too does God inspire awe through His amazing creation and power.

God is Like a Box of Crayons

Macaroni and Cheese

Macaroni and cheese is the ultimate soul food. Dating back to 14th Century cookbooks it has been providing comfort and full bellies for centuries.

We may think of it as a cheap meal in a box now, but in the not-so-distant history, it was a fancy feast for the elite.

Thomas Jefferson was so smitten with the dish that he used his connections to acquire a machine for making macaroni from the French. He also served it at a State dinner during his presidency in 1802.

When factories made the noodles and other ingredients accessible to the everyday man, the elite snubbed their noses at it. Those of us who would not consider ourselves elite rejoice at being able to partake in such a blessing as common folk. The elite's loss is our gain.

All are now free to enjoy the comfort and satisfaction that comes from this lovely soul food. Jesus, too, destroyed the dividing line between who could come to God and be comforted.

> "Remember that the Lord draws no distinction between Jew and Non-Jew - He is Lord over all things and he pours out his treasures on all who invoke His name because Scripture says, "Everyone who calls on the name of the Lord will be saved." - Romans 10:12-13 (The Voice)

Prior to Jesus, only the Jews were God's people. Jesus made the blessings of God accessible to all individuals. The dividing line became who would choose Jesus and who would reject him.

Just like Mac and cheese was once a blessing for only a select few, but is now a meal for the common folk, so too was God's blessing reserved for Jews, but now the ultimate soul food is available for any that would choose it.

God is Like a Box of Crayons

Cornflower

This blue color reflects the flower by the same name. Although beautiful, this flower is actually a weed. It is a plant native to Europe, but although it used to run rampant in the corn and grain fields, hence its name, but now it is no longer reseeding itself naturally because of being tainted by the herbicides man has introduced.

They also call the cornflower the Bachelor's Button. This goes back to when men wore a flower in a buttonhole on their suit to show they were in love or ready for courting.

A more modern practice is for the groom and best man to wear these flowers on the day of the wedding as boutonnieres. History has pegged these flowers as a sign of love, courting, and marriage. It represents that a man is ready to move forward with his bride.

We know from the Bible that Jesus is ready and eager to come back and get His bride. He has gone away to get a home ready for her.

> And if I go and prepare a place for you, I will come back and take you to be with me that you also may be where I am.- John 14:3 (NIV)

The Bible tells us that only God knows when Jesus will return and get us. You can imagine, like an anxious groom, Jesus is pacing excitedly. All of heaven is watching Jesus' passion as He waits. One day, they will celebrate with Him as He returns for His bride.

> Let us be glad and rejoice, and let us give honor to him. For the time has come for the wedding feast of the Lamb, and his bride has prepared herself.
> - Revelation 19:7 (NLT)

Christ is waiting for us to finish preparing for the wedding. He is waiting for us to be an untainted bride, dressed in a white gown, rid of sin, before He can complete the ceremony.

Each time we delay, each time we forsake our beloved by sinning, it breaks God's heart. He wants to present His son to a perfect bride that has saved herself for Him.

> The thing that has me so upset is that I care about you so much—this is the passion of God burning inside me! I promised your hand in marriage to Christ, presented you as a pure virgin to her husband. And now I'm afraid that exactly as the Snake seduced Eve with his smooth tongue, you are being lured away from the simple purity of your love for Christ. - 2 Corinthians 11:1-3 (Message)

Just like bachelors wear a Cornflower to proclaim they are ready for marriage, God too has proclaimed that Jesus is ready to come claim us as His bride. The question is, are we ready for Him?

God is Like a Box of Crayons

God is Like a Box of Crayons

Tan

Tanning has evolved from using the bark of trees that have tannins, to chromium sulfate, to tan the hides. Tannum or oak bark is where we get the name tan.

This entire process of tanning causes the hide to be more flexible and ready for its intended use. The hide is placed on a frame and stretched to its limit then soaked in the tannins of bark, or chemicals coating the collagen, the glue that holds cells together causing it to be less water-soluble and more resistant to bacterial attacks.

Without the stretching and soaking, the hide would be near worthless and decompose. If you attempted to use it, it'd fall apart or contaminate the contents you placed in the hide.

God puts us through a similar process to prepare us for receiving His Holy Spirit and transforming power. He often stretches us to the breaking point. He soaks us in His love, which transforms and coats us so we are more resistant to the decay of sin. God does all this to prepare us for receiving Jesus and the purpose for which He's chosen us.

> "You wouldn't pour new wine into old wineskins. If you did, the skins would burst, the wine would run out, and the wineskins would be ruined. No, you would pour new wine into new wineskins-and both the wine and the wineskins would be preserved." - Matthew 9:17 (voice)

This stretching and pain we are going through in our lives is preparation for the new wine that God is pouring into our hearts. It's eliminating the old way we think. It is making our very cells fit to be a carrier of Christ.

Just like the color tan invokes a thought about the transformation of dead animal skin into leather through tanning, so too does it bring to mind how God takes our dead flesh and gives it new life by preparing us to carry out His purpose and plan.

God is Like a Box of Crayons

God is Like a Box of Crayons

Purple Mountain Majesty

There are landscapes that take your breath away. The sun setting over the ocean, the Grand Canyon, or a rainbow created by an erupting geyser. They named this light purple crayon after a line in a poem titled, "Pikes Peak" by Katharine Lee Bates was inspired by one of those marvels. The poem was later updated and given the name "America the Beautiful" and is one of the most popular patriotic songs in America.

The original words, which have been updated, start out describing the scene that Bates could see from the top of Pikes Peak.

> O great for halcyon skies,
> For amber waves of grain,
> For purple mountain majesties
> Above the enameled plain!
> America! America!
> God shed His grace on thee,
> Till souls wax fair as earth and air
> And music-hearted sea!

From the top of Pikes Peak, on a clear day, you might see five different states. The varying landscape, the compelling mountains, the colors that were chosen, all point to an artist and creator.

Bates used the phrase, "God shed His grace on thee" four times. When she was inspired by what she saw, God was not distant from her mind, but at the forefront.

King David, also inspired bt the mountains, wrote poems and songs about God.

> Come, let us sing for joy to the LORD; let us shout aloud to the Rock of our salvation. 2 Let us come before him with thanksgiving and extol him with music and song. 3 For the LORD is the great God, the great King above all gods. 4 In his hand are the depths of the earth, and the mountain peaks belong to him. 5 The sea is his, for he made it, and his hands formed the dry land.- Psalm 95:1-5 (NIV)

Being at the top of the world, sitting on a mountain, provides a perspective of how big and glorious God really is. The remarkable scenery gives you an idea of the creativity and genius of God. Seeing how the weather, geography and all of nature function together in harmony blows the mind.

> You are glorious and more majestic than the everlasting mountains.
> - Psalm 76:4 (NLT)

Just like the Purple Mountain Majesty color helped paint a picture that inspired Katharine Lee Bates' poem, so too does God inspire poems and songs by taking our breath away.

God is Like a Box of Crayons

God is Like a Box of Crayons

Spring Green

You trudge through the snow; it has a been a long, hard winter, and you are trying to get everything done before the sun goes down. Out of the corner of your vision, something catches your eye.

You stop and dare to hope. Is that? Could it be? It is! The first green shoots of grass are coming up through the snow. It's a sign that winter is ending and better days are ahead.

This is all wrapped up in the color of spring green. Spring is an exciting time of the year. The Earth comes to life again after the long winter. Plants and animals return and multiply.

Most people dislike winter and love spring. Winter represents death and spring with new life and new beginnings. Without the dark winter, we wouldn't appreciate spring as much.

In our lives, it is often the same way. We face hardships, have struggles, and then God brings a season of spring.

There is a time for everything, and a season for every activity under the heavens: 2 a time to be born and a time to die, a time to plant and a time to uproot, 3 a time to kill and a time to heal, a time to tear down and a time to build, 4 a time to weep and a time to laugh, a time to mourn and a time to dance,- Ecclesiastes 3:1-3 (NIV)

No matter how bad things get, we can hold on to God's promise in Revelation.

And I heard a loud voice from the throne saying, "Look! God's dwelling place is now among the people, and he will dwell with them. They will be his people, and God himself will be with them and be their God.

4 'He will wipe every tear from their eyes. There will be no more death or mourning or crying or pain, for the old order of things has passed away."5 He who was seated on the throne said, "I am making everything new!" Then he said, "Write this down, for these words are trustworthy and true." - Revelation 21:3-5 (NIV)

Just like the green of spring brings promise of new beginnings, so too does God bring us the promise of making all things new.

God is Like a Box of Crayons

God is Like a Box of Crayons

Timberwolf

"Run!" There is chaos as your group scatters in every direction, looking for which way to go.

I must not get cut off. You think to yourself. Out of the corner of your eye, you see a gray blur. The mighty timber wolf. You know there are more. Wolves hunt in packs, looking for weak members of their prey's herd. They separate the weak from the rest of the pack and surround it. Some members of the pack will approach the rear, while others attack from the front.

You look behind you. There they are. The clean-up crew. Bristling and growling, the wolves nip at the heals of the slowest and it sends a shudder down your spine. You are bigger than most of them, but you know that by hunting in this fashion, the wolves can take down prey that are much larger. Once the sick and the weak are removed your herd will be stronger. You just hope today you aren't the slowest or sickest.

Jesus warned us,

> Along the way, watch out for false prophets. They will come to you in sheep's clothing, but underneath that quaint and innocent wool, they are hungry wolves.
> - Matthew 7:15 (Voice)

Like wolves, false prophets prey on those that are weak and easily separated from the herd.

> For false Christs shall arise, and false prophets, and will do wonderful miracles so that if it were possible, even God's chosen ones would be deceived.
> - Matthew 24:24 (Living)

We must be firm in our faith and stick close to our brothers and sisters in Christ. We must lean on the promises of God and not be slowed down by sin and stick to the truth.

> So since we stand surrounded by all those who have gone before, an enormous cloud of witnesses, let us drop every extra weight, every sin that clings to us and slackens our pace, and let us run with endurance the long race set before us.
> - Hebrews 12:1 (Voice)

God uses the false prophets as part of his plan to strengthen His herd. God is a wolf destroying the weak vessels so He can save those strong in the faith.

> Even though God desires to demonstrate His anger and to reveal His power, He has shown tremendous restraint toward those vessels of wrath that are doomed to be cracked and shattered.- Romans 9:22 (Voice)

Yet, in his mind-blowing design, God is also how we lose sin so we can escape His wrath.

> The next day John saw Jesus coming toward him and said, "Look! There is the Lamb of God who takes away the world's sin!" - John 1:29 (Living)

God is both the lamb and the wolf. He is the destroyer and the one destroyed to save us. Jesus took on all the sin of the world, became the sickest of us all so God the Father could pour out his wrath onto Him and give us an opportunity to escape.

Just like timber wolves separate off the weakest in the herd, making them stronger, God too removes those bogged down and sick with sin to give us a chance to escape.

God is Like a Box of Crayons

God is Like a Box of Crayons

Sienna

There are two different colors with the name Sienna in the crayon box. Raw sienna and burnt sienna. Raw sienna is a dullish brown and burnt sienna has rich undertones of red in it.

These colors are valued very differently. Raw sienna was described "dull as dirt" by a writer assigned an article about the color. Yet, in contrast, it has been said that burnt sienna is the most useful color on a painter's pallet.

To get the burnt sienna pigment, you start with raw sienna and cook it. The pigment goes through a chemical process that transforms the dull as dirt raw sienna into the most versatile and useful color for an artist.

Turning raw sienna into burnt sienna is like baking pottery. The transformation is as well. You go from having something fairly useless, wet clay, transformed into a beautiful and useful pot. The high heat removes various toxins and changes the elements that make up the material.

In our own lives, God is taking us and putting us through a transformation.

"And I will put this third into the fire, and refine them as one refines silver, and test them as gold is tested. They will call upon my name and I will answer them. I will say, "They are my people and they will say The Lord is my God." - Zechariah 13:9 (ESV)

God refines us through tough times,

"Behold I have refined you, but not as silver, I have tried you in the furnace of affliction." - Isaiah 48:10 (ESV)

This entire process of being burned and refined through affliction is to prepare us to carry the message of God inside of us. It is to transform us into the vessels He desires.

"If only you look at us, you might well miss the brightness. We carry this precious Message around in the unadorned clay pots of our ordinary lives. That's to prevent anyone from confusing God's incomparable power with us. As it is there's not much chance of that. You know for yourselves that we're not much to look at."
- 2 Corinthians 4:7-10 (Message)

Just like the dull color, raw sienna, is turned into the most useful color on a painter's pallet, so too does God use fire to transform us into useful clay pots that carry His message.

God is Like a Box of Crayons

God is Like a Box of Crayons

Chestnut

Chestnut is a dark tan with a reddish tin. This color is named after the chestnut tree.

There is a story in Genesis 30 that talks of it. Jacob is working for Laban, his father-in-law, and basically has asked for a raise. He's worked 14 years for the right to marry Laban's daughter (two actually) and now he wants to get paid for taking care of Laban's flock. God has blessed Laban under Jacob's care, and now Jacob has a proposal for Laban.

> "Let me go through your flocks today and remove from them every speckled or spotted sheep, every dark-colored lamb and every spotted or speckled goat. They will be my wages." - Genesis 30:32 (ESV)

They come to an agreement, but things are not as they seem. Laban tricked by Jacob before. Laban got Jacob to work for seven years when he switched which daughter Jacob was going to marry at the last second. Jacob devises a plan to profit from this new arrangement.

We see it play out in a later verse,

> "And Jacob took him rods of green poplar, and of the hazel and chestnut tree, and pulled white strakes in them and made the white appear which was in the rods... And the flocks conceived before the rods, and brought forth cattle ringstraked, speckled, and spotted." - Genesis 30:37-39 (KJV)

So Jacob does this only when the strongest of the flock are near and in doing so amasses the best for himself, because he has marked them with the bark of the chestnut.

Jesus also is claiming sheep for Himself by stealing souls back from the ruler of this land, Satan. God is putting His mark on people that He is selecting.

> "In him you also, when you heard the word of truth, the gospel of your salvation, and believed in him, were sealed with the promised Holy Spirit, who is the guarantee of our inheritance until we acquire possessions of it, to the praise of his glory." - Ephesians 1:13-14

Just like the chestnut was able to mark the lambs that Jacon wanted for his flock, so too is the Holy Spirit able to mark those God wants to be in His eternal flock.

God is Like a Box of Crayons

God is Like a Box of Crayons

Salmon

Feel you are swimming against the current today? Well, then you are in good company. I'd like to introduce you to the color salmon. It is named after the fish of the same name.

These fish are remarkable creatures. They are born upriver in a bed of gravel. They live in this freshwater environment for three years before moving into a brackish environment for a time and then finishing their trip to the saltwater environment of the Pacific ocean.

The most astounding thing that salmon do, and claim to fame, is at the end of their life, they return to their river of birth by swimming... upstream.

Not only is this strenuous, imagine jumping over rocks, avoiding bears, and eagles while fighting the current of the river, but ultimately this ends in their death.

Once the salmon return to their birthplace, they spawn the next generation of eggs and die. Their cause of death is the deterioration of their body because of the return to freshwater. If the salmon didn't fight the stream and give their bodies up for death, the next generation would not be born.

> "...have the same mindset as Christ Jesus Who being in the very nature God, did not consider equality with God something to be used to his own advantage, rather he made himself nothing by taking the very nature of a servant, being made in human likeness. And being found in appearance as a man he humbled himself by becoming obedient to death - even death on a cross.- Philippians 2:5-8 (NIV)

> You know the grace that has come to us through our Lord Jesus the Anointed. He set aside His infinite riches and was born into the lowest circumstance so that you may gain great riches through His humble poverty. - 2 Corinthians 8:9 (Voice)

If Jesus didn't lay his life down, if He didn't give himself up for us, we would never have a path to eternal life.

> There will be a highway called the Holy Road. No one rude or rebellious is permitted on this road. It's for God's people exclusively—   impossible to get lost on this road. Not even fools can get lost on it. No lions on this road,   no dangerous wild animals — Nothing and no one dangerous or threatening.   Only the redeemed will walk on it. The people God has ransomed will come back on this road. They'll sing as they make their way home to Zion,   unfading halos of joy encircling their heads, Welcomed home with gifts of joy and gladness as all sorrows and sighs scurry into the night. - Isaiah 35:8-10 (Message)

> And He will be leading you. He'll be with you, and He'll never fail you or abandon you. So don't be afraid! - Deuteronomy 31:8 (Voice)

Just like salmon swim against the flow and go to certain death to bring about new life, so too did Jesus go against all logic, leaving his heavenly environment giving up his life on the cross so we could have eternal life with Him.

When you feel you are swimming upstream in the world, remember that Jesus went out before you and is right there swimming with you, don't be discouraged.

God is Like a Box of Crayons

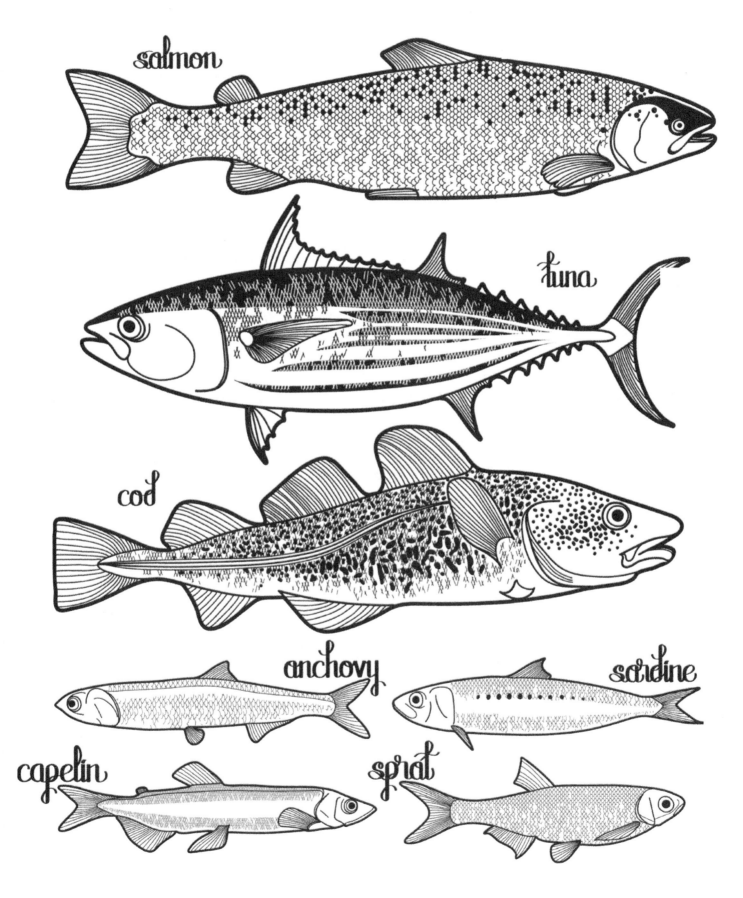

God is Like a Box of Crayons

Scarlet

Israel is camped outside of the city of Jericho. They have had the hand of God leading the way and giving them victory over other nations. The city of Jericho is frightened of what Israel and their God will do to them.

The leader of Israel, Joshua, sends spies to scout out the city. They encounter a woman named Rahab. The Bible identifies her as a prostitute. She helps the spies hide and even lies to her king in Joshua 2:2-5 so they are kept safe.

She tells the spies,

> We have heard how the Lord dried up the water of the Red Sea for you when you came out of Egypt, and what you did to Sihon and Og, the two kings of the Amorites east of the Jordan, whom you completely destroyed. 11 When we heard of it, our hearts melted in fear and everyone's courage failed because of you, for the Lord your God is God in heaven above and on the earth below.- Joshua 2:10-11 (NIV)

A powerful statement from someone who doesn't know God, but only knows of God. The Bible calls her, "Rahab the prostitute." How would you like your sin to be how you are remembered? The good news is that the story doesn't stop there.

Rahab begs the spies to tell her that the Lord will show kindness to her while helping them escape. The spies give their word and tell Rahab what she and her family must do to be saved from the coming destruction.

> We will keep the oath we have sworn to you, but 18 only if you will follow these instructions: Gather all of your family here in this house, and tie this scarlet cord in the window where you let us down.- Joshua 2:17:18 (Voice)

God destroys the city of Jericho and spares Rahab and her family.

Not only does God save Rahab the prostitute, but He includes her in His royal lineage. He wiped out her title of sin and put her in a place of honor because of her belief.

Just like a scarlet rope saved Rahab and her family from destruction, so too is Jesus, our scarlet rope. If we acknowledge and accept Him as our salvation, He'll wipe away our sin and call us sons and daughters as part of His family tree.

God is Like a Box of Crayons

God is Like a Box of Crayons

Mauve

This is a color with a rich history. This purple has been used to define an entire decade of history. The 1890s is called the Mauve Decade.

It is all thanks to a young man named Sir William Perkins. In 1856, he attempted to cure malaria when, by accident, he invented a purple dye that became known as mauve.

Sir William Perkins successfully promoted the dye to the businesses in the industry. By 1890, it was the most popular color for clothing.

Perkins accidental discovery brightened up the clothing of the day, but that was just a by-product of his original mission, curing a disease.

Often in our own lives, we look to God and ask him to fix our situation, our circumstances, to brighten up our life. We know we should be happier with Christ in our hearts, but we don't feel happy. The world beats us down, our sin eats away at us, and life can be hard.

I think it is important to remember that while Jesus brings amazing joy to our spirits and can improve our lives, that is NOT why he came.

> "Here's a statement worthy of trust. Jesus the Annointed, the Liberating King, came into the world to save sinners..." - 1 Timothy 1:15

> "Think not that I am come to send peace on earth: I came not to send [or bring] peace, but a sword."- Matthew 10:34

Jesus came to cure a disease called sin. He came to save us from that sin.

> "Jesus said to him, "Today salvation has come to this house, because this man, too is a son of Abraham. For the Son of Man came to seek and to save the lost."
> - Luke 19:9-10

It is because we are no longer lost, no longer dead to sin that we should celebrate, that we should feel joy, that we should feel happy.

> Though you have not seen him, you love him; and even though you do not see him now, you believe in him and are filled with an inexpressible and glorious joy, 9 for you are receiving the end result of your faith, the salvation of your souls.
> - 1 Peter 1:8-9 (NIV)

Just like Sir William Perkins accidentally discovered the happy color mauve while trying to cure a disease, so too did Jesus brighten up our lives through His eradication of the disease of sin.

God is Like a Box of Crayons

God is Like a Box of Crayons

Sky Blue

The sky is blue, or is it? With color being nothing more than light reflecting into our eyes, the reality is the sky isn't blue. We are simply seeing the blue light waves being reflected off the gas and particles in our atmosphere.

Sir Isaac Newton first discovered how light, when refracted or scattered, produces colors. By placing a prism in his window, he produced a magnificent color spectrum twenty-two feet onto a wall. To prove that the prism was not coloring the light, Isaac Newton refracted the light back together with a 2nd prism. The light does not achieve this color array until the light has been scattered.

Jesus told us we were "the light of the world" and that we should reach the entire world with the gospel. Throughout history, God has used persecution to get Christians to spread the gospel by fleeing.
The early church was hunkered down in Jerusalem, waiting for Jesus to return, and Saul came and persecuted the church. The result is God's design.

> On that day a great persecution broke out against the church in Jerusalem, and all except the apostles were scattered throughout Judea and Samaria. 2 Godly men buried Stephen and mourned deeply for him. 3 But Saul began to destroy the church. Going from house to house, he dragged off both men and women and put them in prison. 4 Those who had been scattered preached the word wherever they went. - Acts 8:1-4

Persecution is a way that colors the world with the gospel of Christ. God uses it to move us out of our comfort zone and rely on Him.

God unites us who are scattered around the world preaching and believing in Christ through a single mission, a single purpose, a single person named Jesus Christ. They prophesied during Jesus' time that this would take place even by the Jews that wanted to kill him.

> He did not say this on his own; as high priest at that time he was led to prophesy that Jesus would die for the entire nation. 52 And not only for that nation, but to bring together and unite all the children of God scattered around the world.
> - John 11:51-52 (NLT)

Once the job is over, Jesus will gather all of us scattered colors back together.

> He'll come down from heaven and the dead in Christ will rise—they'll go first. Then the rest of us who are still alive at the time will be caught up with them into the clouds to meet the Master. Oh, we'll be walking on air! And then there will be one huge family reunion with the Master. So reassure one another with these words.
> - 1 Thessalonians 4:17 (Message)

Just like the sky is blue because the colors of light are being scattered by the atmosphere, so too does God use the atmosphere of persecution to scatter us.

Be reassured, He is going to gather us colors from around the world and bring us back together and we'll all meet up at sky blue to go home!

God is Like a Box of Crayons

God is Like a Box of Crayons

Final Thoughts

As we discovered together in this book, God has called us to give His world colors.

"Here's another way to put it: You're here to be light, bringing out the God-colors in the world. Matthew 5:14 (Message)

Too often we as Christ-followers paint God as black and white, right or wrong, but we are called to shine light and let the colors reveal themselves to whoever encounters them. We need to let the colors be what the colors are. Instead of judging whether something is right or wrong, we can simply shine into the situation with the light Jesus has given us and the truth will be revealed.

When people encounter images and pictures they are more likely to remember a picture that is colored than when something is white and black. By presenting the world with more light we are bringing out the God-colors to make it easier for others to remember Him. This is a powerful and exciting calling. The question becomes how do we shine our light? What does that look like?

You are like that illuminating light. Let your light shine everywhere you go, that you may illumine creation, so men and women everywhere may see your good actions, may see creation at its fullest, may see your devotion to Me, and may turn and praise your Father in heaven because of it. - Matthew 5:16 (Voice)

It is through our devotion, through our God-inspired actions that the world will see the light and glorify God. If we shine this light we will fulfill our purpose on Earth and God will separate us from the darkness and bring us into His presence.

And God saw that the light was good. And God separated the light from the darkness.- Genesis 1:4 (ESV)

It is my hope that this devotional helped increase your devotion to God and has given you a brighter day. If I succeeded in brightening your day I'd be honored if you left a review of the book wherever you purchased this book by heading to GodisLikea.com/crayonreview/.

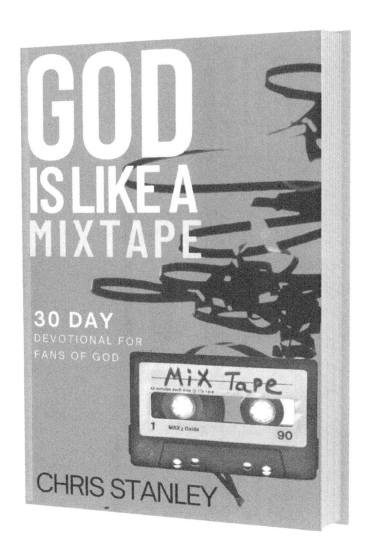

Get a Free Devotional by Heading to

GodisLikea.com/free/

Get our God Is Like a Mixtape devotional book for free when you join the "God is Like" email list.

Also in the God is Like Devotional Series

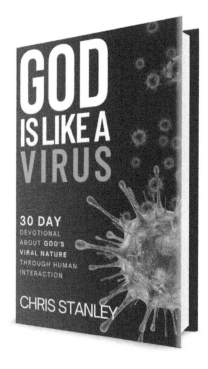

Find all of our Devotional Books at
GodisLikea.com

Made in the USA
Coppell, TX
09 December 2021